The Christmas Kitten

by S.J. Hearn

Illustrated by Melanie Mitchell

SCHOLASTIC

As the season starts to change,
Near the end of every year,
When fall begins to slip away,
And Christmastime is near...

Santa starts to check his list
For children naughty and nice—
A job this big needs help, you see,
Even Santa needs advice.

The elves are busy tinkering,
Singing, and toymaking.
Moms and dads are busy, too,
Preparing treats and baking.

But, Santa has some special friends
On which he can rely.
Out his little helpers go
To keep a watchful eye.

Cross your fingers really tight
And say the word "noel."
And then just listen carefully
For the tinkling of a bell.

You just might find a furry friend
Sent for you from Santa Claus,
A snow-white kitten from the north,
With magic in its paws!

She's come to bring you laughter
And spread her Christmas cheer,
To make your Christmas wishes
Come true throughout the year.

Please be sure to welcome her—
Your home she'd like to share.
Tell your kitten all your dreams
And show her that you care.

With boys and girls, big and small,
Your kitten wants to play.
Her favorite game is hide-and-seek.
Where could she be today?

As gifts are made and presents wrapped,
And placed beneath the tree,
You just might hear your kitten's bell,
Never know where she might be.

Your kitten watches carefully
As you and your friends play,
For how you treat your family,
In deeds and things you say.

Every night, when you're asleep,
In return for all your trust,
Your kitten reports to Santa
In a poof of snowy dust.

Your kitten will be with you
'Til late on Christmas Eve.
When you fall fast asleep,
It's time for her to leave.

Before you close your eyes and sleep,
There's one last thing to do.
Your little kitten needs a name,
A gift for her from you.

A name makes all things special
Because no one is the same,
For your kitten to come back next year.
She needs the purr-fect name.

As lamps and lights go out at night
And bedroom curtains close,
For one last time, there's magic
When a special north wind blows.

So be kind to all, be good and true,
Keep full of Christmas cheer.
Your kitten will be back again
The same time every year.

Written by S.J. Hearn
Illustrated by Melanie Mitchell

an imprint of
SCHOLASTIC
www.scholastic.com

Scholastic and Tangerine Press and associated logos are trademarks of Scholastic Inc.

Published by Tangerine Press, an imprint of Scholastic Inc., 557 Broadway, New York, NY 10012

Scholastic Canada, Ltd., Markham, Ontario

10 9 8 7 6 5 4 3 2 1

ISBN: 978-0-545-77517-5

Printed and bound in Jiaxing, China
403742 6/14